The role and place of w   ...g. ...e. ....y systems

Muwo Mbwene Jean Claude

The role and place of women in agroforestry systems

ScienciaScripts

Imprint

Any brand names and product names mentioned in this book are subject to trademark, brand or patent protection and are trademarks or registered trademarks of their respective holders. The use of brand names, product names, common names, trade names, product descriptions etc. even without a particular marking in this work is in no way to be construed to mean that such names may be regarded as unrestricted in respect of trademark and brand protection legislation and could thus be used by anyone.

Cover image: www.ingimage.com

This book is a translation from the original published under ISBN 978-613-8-42455-0.

Publisher:
Sciencia Scripts
is a trademark of
Dodo Books Indian Ocean Ltd. and OmniScriptum S.R.L publishing group

120 High Road, East Finchley, London, N2 9ED, United Kingdom
Str. Armeneasca 28/1, office 1, Chisinau MD-2012, Republic of Moldova, Europe

ISBN: 978-620-7-30142-3

TABLE OF CONTENTS:

CHAPTER 1 7

CHAPTER 2 15

CHAPTER 3 20

CHAPTER 4 27

DEDICATION

To all the women farmers in the Democratic Republic of Congo,

I dedicate this work.

Jean Claude MUWO

ACKNOWLEDGEMENTS

Our special thanks go to Professor Jean de Dieu MINENGU of the Faculty of Agronomic Sciences at the University of Kinshasa, for all the advice and scientific supervision he provided during this research.

We are very grateful to the authorities and staff of the Nstio project for opening the doors and welcoming us into their institution to make this research possible.

SUMMARY

The main objective of this study is to promote the involvement of women in agroforestry. Specifically, the study aims to analyse the contribution of agroforestry to women's emancipation.

Thus, a survey was conducted during the period from 23 October to 23 November 2017 within the Nstio project, among 30 randomly selected households. This survey consisted of collecting information to verify the level of women's involvement in the Nstio agroforestry project.

The results of our study show that 76.6% of women own the land, compared with 23.3% of men. With regard to the distribution of activities within the farm, of the six activities identified during our study, women are responsible for five main activities: planting, maintenance, harvesting, processing agricultural products and selling. Men, on the other hand, are only responsible for preparing the land.

In view of this unequal distribution of activities throughout the production cycle, it is clearly established that the heavy responsibility in this agroforestry system falls on the woman, and in these conditions, the productivity of the farm will not live up to expectations.

We suggest that further studies be carried out to find the strategies needed to strengthen the position of women in the management of agroforestry operations.

Key words: Gender, agroforestry, production cycle, Batéké Plateau.

INTRODUCTION

Context

In the Democratic Republic of Congo (DRC), agriculture contributes around 40% of GDP. Agriculture is essentially subsistence farming, practised on small individual and/or family farms. The rural population accounts for 70% of the country's total population, and 60% of this rural population works in the agricultural sector. Women account for 51% of the rural population, and 85% of them work in the agricultural sector (Folly, 2013).

Slash-and-burn agriculture as practised in the DRC and attempts to copy the production system that emerged from the Green Revolution are no longer capable of ensuring food security, creating wealth for farmers and protecting our common heritage, the climate. The economic, energy, food and ecological crises all call for a paradigm shift in agricultural production and food consumption (Tchunza, 2010).

Establishing an innovative agroforestry system in the savannah increases agricultural production and protects the soil and forests.

Agroforestry makes it possible to protect the forest, increase agricultural production and help combat global warming, firstly by sequestering greenhouse gases (CO_2) through afforestation and reforestation (planting fruit trees, fast-growing species, etc.), *and* secondly by avoiding deforestation.

With this in mind, a number of projects have been set up to improve farmers' incomes throughout the country in general, and in Kinshasa (Plateau des Batéké) in particular, through agroforestry. The aim of these initiatives is to combat the high level of unemployment in rural areas, the migration of farmers to urban areas and, above all, to improve production.

These projects also aim to train farmers in agroforestry and reforestation techniques with a view to restoring soil fertility (Tchunza, 2010).

Reforestation efforts have reduced the exploitation of natural forests and contributed to the reappearance of previously endemic animal species, notably wild pigs and antelopes. These programmes have led to an increase in peasant agricultural

3

production; manioc production has increased fivefold in some regions, and new sources of income have emerged, such as honey and charcoal production (CADIM, 2010).

Issues

In agriculture, production tasks are carried out by men and women, according to social and cultural rules, and even religious beliefs. In agro-industrial sectors, for example, women and men have specific roles throughout the production, processing and marketing chain.

However, taking gender into account in agricultural development projects has positive consequences for production, land and food security, and therefore for the success of the projects (FAO, 2011).

The DRC's National Gender Policy aims to create a socio-economic and institutional environment conducive to gender equity. This ambition still needs to be realised in the various development sectors. More specifically, women farmers continue to face numerous constraints to their economic empowerment, in a context of subsistence farming, practised on an individual and family scale, and affected by climate change. These constraints include discrimination in sustainable and secure access to land, poor technical support and discrimination in access to information technology, limited access to agricultural credit, and difficulties in accessing high value-added activities and markets.

Approximately 170 km east of the city of Kinshasa (Batéké Plateau), there are three major agroforestry projects, including: (i) the 100,000-hectare plantation at Mampu, divided into 25-hectare blocks and allocated to 320 farming families.

Three agroforestry activities are practised in this artificial forest, namely beekeeping, agriculture and carbonisation (Bisiaux *et al.*, 2014); (ii) the Ibi village agroforestry plantations in a vast community agroforestry programme managed by a local NGO, GI-Agro (Groupe d'Initiatives pour l'Agroforesterie en Afrique), the aim of which is to increase farmers' incomes; and (iii) the Ntsio project, which aims to contribute to the fight against poverty among the urban and rural population by increasing supply on the capital's food and wood energy markets, developing diversified agroforestry over an

4

area of 5.500 ha on the Batéké Plateau through the involvement of an organised community.

Research questions

What is the contribution of agroforestry practices to women's emancipation? What is the level of women's involvement in the different phases of these projects? What are the specific difficulties that limit women's involvement in agroforestry projects?

Assumptions

Certain agroforestry practices can contribute to the empowerment of women in the socio-economic and environmental conditions of the Batéké Plateau. Identifying specific difficulties is an important step in the process of empowering women.

Objectives

The main objective of this study is to promote the involvement of women in agroforestry. Specifically, the study aims to analyse the contribution of agroforestry to women's emancipation.

Interest in the subject

This study will help to improve the design, development and implementation of agroforestry projects from the point of view of representativeness and the distribution of activities between women and men. The study will also make it possible to build up the database needed to develop future agroforestry projects.

Delimitation in time and space

This study was conducted in the eastern part of the Province of Kinshasa/Plateau des Batéké, during the period from 23 October to 23 November 2017. More specifically, it focused on the Ntsio agroforestry project in the Mongata and Mwe groups.

Labour division

In addition to the introduction and conclusion, this work comprises three chapters:

  The first deals with the literature review;

  The second describes the environment, the equipment used and the methods employed;

The third section presents the results of the study and a discussion.

CHAPTER 1

LUTERATURE REVIEW

1.1. Overview of agroforestry

1.1.1. Origin

Agroforestry (AF) encompasses many traditional land-use systems, such as market gardens, boundary tree plantations (bocages), shifting cultivation, shrub fallow systems and contour farming. African multi-storey agriculture and trees, such as African gardens and orchards (Dupriez and de Leener 1993), are part of this age-old tradition. Alley cropping was developed by research in the late 1970s to eliminate the need for a fallow period in the humid and sub-humid tropics in order to rebuild soil fertility. It is used in many African countries, including Burkina Faso, Ethiopia, Guinea, Kenya, Rwanda and Burundi. All African countries south of the Sahara practise agroforestry. Today, new forms of agroforestry are emerging, responding to the constraints of today's agricultural systems. The main changes compared with traditional agroforestry concern the choice of tree species, the layout of the trees and their density (Anonymous, 2010).

1.1.2. Definitions of concepts

Agroforestry is an intentional, intensive, integrated and interactive system that tends towards a point of equilibrium. The aim and raison d'être of agroforestry systems is to optimise positive interactions so as to obtain higher, more diversified and more sustained total production from available resources, under existing ecological, technological and socio-economic conditions.

As a science, or rather a scientific approach, **agroforestry** is the study of interfaces and their variations in time and space between woody plants and other soil productions (animal and/or plant). It is not the exclusive domain of agriculture or forestry.

Agroforestry (AF) is therefore not a single technology, but covers a general concept of trees in crop and livestock systems to achieve multifunctionality.

There is no clear dividing line between FF and forestry, nor between FF and agriculture. The factors that influence the performance of FA are the types and mixes of agricultural crops, livestock and trees, the genetic material, the number and

7

distribution of trees, the age of the trees, the management of crops, livestock and trees, and the climate.

1.1.3. Typology of Agroforestry Systems

Agroforestry ranges from very simple to very complex and dense systems, many of which are traditional land-use systems. The main agroforestry systems listed to date are: windbreaks, riparian buffer strips, intercropping systems (ICS), silvopastoral systems, crops grown under forest cover, alleycropping, multi-storey systems, agroforestry park systems, tree-covered riparian buffer strips, agroforestry intercropping systems, agroforestry park systems, improved fallows, fodder banks, market gardens, shrub and tree fallows, etc.

1.2. Importance of agroforestry

1.2.1. Ecological importance

1.2.1.1. In relation to the ground

Agroforestry allows mineral elements to be recycled from deep in the soil and brought to the surface to be made available to crops. Agroforestry adds organic matter to the soil in the form of falling litter, and in particular sustains the soil's microbial life. It also combats soil erosion and land degradation, increases the availability of water in the soil and improves soil cover.

1.2.1.2. In relation to the climate

FA leads to favourable changes in microclimatic and agroclimatic conditions (e.g. shade trees that can reduce extreme temperatures by around 5°C, windbreaks), reduces pressure on forests and also promotes long-term carbon sequestration and a reduction in CO_2 emissions (above and below ground). AF therefore increases resilience to climate change.

1.2.1.3. Other ecological importance

The agroforestry system supports a number of ecosystem services, such as increasing species diversity and habitat diversity. It promotes natural wood tissues and improved biodiversity. It provides biological control of pests and diseases. In short, it increases the health of the ecosystem.

1.2.2. Socio-economic importance

The trees used in agroforestry are multi-purpose woody plants that provide a wide range of income and products, including food for human consumption, fodder for animals, wood for construction, energy, paper, pollen for bees, job creation, etc. (Berti and Lebailly, 2012).

1.3. Type

1.3.1. concept definitions

According to the UN, **gender refers to** the socio-cultural construction of masculine and feminine roles and of relations between men and women; gender describes culturally assimilated and inculcated social functions.

Gender differs from other development concepts in that it addresses the root causes of social inequalities, namely social relationships. In fact, life in society requires the establishment of reference standards with which the different social categories (men, women, young, old) identify in order to work together. **Gender is** none other than these rules and regulations that govern social relations in a given community (UN-WOMEN, 2014).

The concept of **"gender" needs to be** qualified with the concept of parity, which consists of equality of status or functional equivalence. The concept of parity forms the basis of policies to combat inequality between women and men. In the name of this principle, a number of laws have been enacted to reduce disparities in pay, employment, education, women's representation in bodies of political and economic power, etc. (UN-WOMEN, 2014).

Feminism is a current of ideas calling for equal rights for men and women through a collective movement to improve the status and place of women in society and the fight for equal rights for men and women.

Emancipation is the action of freeing oneself from a bond, a hindrance, a state of dependence, domination or prejudice. **Parity is** equal representation of men and women in all related bodies.

9

1.3.2. Gender in Africa

In recent years, some progress has been made in taking the gender dimension into account in development interventions in Africa. Gender represents an evolution in human-centred development concepts. This approach marks an important change and renews the different approaches to development problems. Gender is a concept that is trying to take root in analyses, reflections and actions relating to development cooperation in Africa.

Most African countries want to ensure that any analysis, initiative or development project takes into account the fact that societies and human activities are divided between two types of individuals, men and women.

In sectors such as agriculture, the "Gender and Development" approach attempts to establish, on the basis of social relations between the sexes, the links between production and reproduction in order to find the source of women's marginalisation and low production (UN-WOMEN, 2014).

The economic role of women is more important in Africa than in other regions, especially in the agricultural sector (Anonymous, 2005). This role tends to go unnoticed and undervalued, yet in Africa, agriculture and the informal sector are dominated by women, but their access to financial services is very limited, and productivity and production are very low (Tshibilondi, 2005).

The existence of a systematic bias against women in terms of access to health, education and other basic social services, the application of proactive support for the systematic participation of women in policy dialogue, economic and sectoral analysis, and the design and implementation of development projects, especially those relating to agriculture, remains a critical issue and a challenge for the development of African countries.

Poverty in Africa has an important gender dimension, where the burden of women's time at work (and the choices associated with it) is disproportionately high compared to men. Gender discrimination limits their participation and reinforces the major inequalities that exist in the exercise of power. It is therefore important to invest in women's economic capacity and productivity, particularly in the agricultural sector.

1.3.3. Gender in the Democratic Republic of Congo (DRC)

1.3.3.1. The status of Congolese women in traditional society

During the colonial period, the Belgian colonists in charge of the administration of the new state applied to Congolese women the concept of the place and role of women in the family and in society that they had in their own country. At that time, the concepts of gender and parity were not yet part of the requirements of democracy. What's more, the introduction of salaried work, reserved exclusively for men in urban centres, weakened Congolese women.

Towards the end of the colonial era, a timid start was made in opening up schools to girls, which accelerated their entry into economic life outside the home through access to mainly female trades, and improved their working conditions.

1.3.3.2. Current situation of women in rural areas

The gender profile confirms the difficult situation of women in rural areas, as a result of socio-political crises, sexual violence in conflict zones, family break-up, survival through informal work, economic dependence, domestic violence, etc. It also shows the central role played by women in all agricultural activities. It also shows the central role played by women in all agricultural activities, and reveals a number of "gender disparities" specific to the sector that have a strong impact on the development of agriculture, as set out below:

(i) Domestic chores, such as collecting water and wood, were left entirely to the women.

(ii) Peasant women are dependent on their husbands to manage their income. Husbands often squander money and hit their wives when they make complaints, but this dependence diminishes as the level of education increases.

(iii) Girls are not free to choose their husbands (as is the case in many tribes in the DRC).

(iv) Traditional land law defines the rules for transferring land, from which women are excluded.

(v) Women are under-represented in agricultural extension services and rarely benefit from the services of support structures.

In other cases, agricultural supervisors addressed the head of the family rather than the farmers. This attitude excludes women from advisory services, but nowadays advisory services are available to both men and women.

1.3.4. Gender in the agricultural sector

Despite the central role played by women in the agricultural sector and the difficulties they face, the new agricultural code promulgated in 2008 to boost the agricultural sector contains no provisions on gender, nor does it mention the difficulties faced by rural women in gaining access to land, agricultural credit or training. The same is true of Law No. 11/022 on the fundamental principles relating to agriculture, enacted in 2011.

1.3.5. Gender in the forestry sector

The FAO has carried out a study on gender mainstreaming in the forestry sector in the DRC, mainly in the city and province of Kinshasa and more briefly in the provinces of Central Kongo, Equateur, North Kivu and South Kivu (FAO, 2007).

The main conclusions of this study are as follows:

(i) Women make a significant contribution to the formal and informal forestry sectors, particularly in agroforestry, reforestation and forest protection and conservation. As such, they play a decisive role in the management and use of forest resources.

(ii) The number of women working in the forestry sector is very low. There are only 13 female managers out of a total of 163 women working in forestry companies.

(iii) A number of structures and networks promote the advancement of women, but the level of integration of women into these structures and their level of support are relatively low, hence the need to strengthen the capacities of these structures in order to make their actions more effective and visible.

To ensure that women are effectively involved in forest management, the study makes the following proposals (FAO, 2007): (i) Carry out fundamental actions to change mentalities and awareness, (ii) Improve the acquisition of knowledge and the circulation of information, (iii) Develop education and awareness-raising for women in the sustainable management of forest resources, (iv) Develop master plans for integrating women's issues into the forestry sector, (v) Improve the representativeness of women in the sector, (vi) Restructure and strengthen management institutions with the aim of improving the participation and coordination of women's actions, (vii) Plan amendments to current legislation so as to reduce its exclusive aspect, which is sometimes inconsistent with modern principles of natural resource management.

1.3.6. Gender in the property sector

Traditional Congolese society was generally governed by a system of patriarchy in which women remained under the tutelage of the men of the clan, and then of their spouse.

Land is therefore inherited from fathers to sons (patrilineal) or from mothers to daughters (matrilineal). In the patrilineal system, which is more common, a woman cannot become the owner of land; she only receives the right of use granted to her by her husband, father or brother in the case of single women, or by her father, father-in-law or brother in the case of widows.

This right of use can be revoked at any time, whereas property rights that can be inherited by men can only be transferred by the state, or even by the customary chief if he has great authority. In matrilineal society, inheritance is based on female lineage, but the granting of use rights is generally placed under the authority of men (brothers and uncles of female heirs). However, there are cases where the land chiefs are women.

1.3.7. The social situation of rural women

Socially, women are more valued for their reproductive role as wives and mothers of large families, especially sons, in a patrilineal system, which they give to the lineage. Her status as a woman, wife and mother is never contested. It is her productive role that is not sufficiently taken into account, even though her investment enables the survival of the family and the construction of the African continent. Any action that has an impact on the household will therefore have an impact on gender. Gender approaches must not lose sight of this, otherwise they run the risk of missing out on the most powerful levers for improving the situation of women (Kloeppinger *et al.,* 2010).

In short, the intellectual and professional capacities of Congolese women are not sufficiently recognised. Women are entrusted with unqualified, unproductive and mind-numbing jobs. While decision-making positions are often the preserve of men. They invest mainly in the informal sector, which makes a considerable economic contribution to family survival, and are heavily involved in agriculture.

Of course, the traditional proverb still applies, namely that "the hen does not crow before the cock". Nevertheless, the Beijing conference has raised or strengthened awareness of the importance of education, and the many associations it has spawned may accentuate this awareness (Lallau, 2004).

1.3.8. Legal status of Congolese women

As for equal rights for men and women, the general principle of Congolese social legislation refutes discrimination based on sex: "For equal work and equal performance, men and women have the same rights and the same obligations". Under equal conditions of work, qualification and performance, all workers are entitled to equal pay, regardless of their origin, sex or age. In practice, however, this principle is not respected.

So all these egalitarian laws are only valid in principle. They remain a pious hope in the practice of a fundamentally macho society. It therefore appears that the advancement of the status of African women in general, and Congolese women in particular, depends not only on the reform of legislation, but also and above all on a change in the conservative mentalities of women and men.

CHAPTER 2
MATERIALS AND METHODS

2.1. . Presentation of the study site

2.1.1. . Geographical location of the Nstio agroforestry estate

Nstio is a village located 180 km from the centre of Kinshasa on the banks of the Kwango river.

The geographical coordinates taken at the centre of the project give the following indications: South latitude: 04°22'11.7"; East longitude: 016° 28'09.5" and; Altitude: 688 m.

The Nstio project is made up of four associations or groups of farmers: (i) the MUDIANKULU association made up of 71 farmers, (ii) the WOLIMBWA association made up of 70 farmers, (iii) the MUSTHIO association made up of 55 farmers and (iv) the DUALE association made up of 63 farmers.

The first two associations are located to the north of the Ntsio project and the other two to the south. There are 260 families in these four associations.

The total surface area of the NSTIO estate is 5,500 ha and the entire site has been reforested with various trees (acacia and others) associated with food crops (manioc, maize, etc.), industrial crops (oil palm) and market garden produce (aubergines, chillies, etc.).

The main objective of the project is to make a significant contribution to the fight against poverty among the local population by increasing the supply of wood and energy to the capital's markets. To achieve this, the project is counting on the involvement of its primary beneficiaries, the farmers who have recently settled on the 5,500-hectare site.

These farmers were selected on the basis of a list (from the villages) submitted by the traditional chiefs who had made the land available to the project.

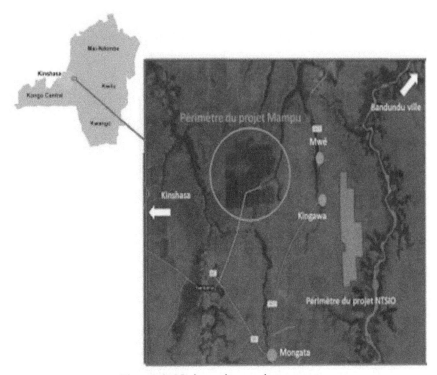

Figure 1: Nstio project perimeter

2.1.2. . Climate

According to Koppen's classification, the climate of the Batékés plateau is Aw4. This is a humid tropical Sudanian climate with two very distinct seasons, a dry season running from mid-May to mid-September and a wet season beginning in mid-September and ending in mid-May, with a short dry season from mid-January to March (Bultot, 1950). Annual rainfall varies between 1,300 and 1,600 mm, with a bimodal distribution that is unevenly distributed throughout the year.

The average annual temperature is 25.7°C, with the highest monthly average (27.1°C) occurring in April, while July is the coldest month of the year, with an average temperature of around 23.2°C.

2.1.3. . Pedology

The soils of Kinshasa in general, and those of the Plateau des Batékés in particular, have a sandy texture with alluvial grains, and vary in colour in places. The average

16

particle size composition of topsoil is 3.4% clay, 5.6% silt and 91.0% sand, with an apparent density of around 1.25 (Makoko *et al.*, 1994).

2.1.4. . Vegetation

The vegetation of the Batéké Plateau consists mainly of shrub savannas alternating with grassy savannas.

The savannahs of the Batéké Plateau are subdivided into five types: grassy savannah, shrub savannah, tree savannah, wooded savannah and steppe savannah (Makoko *et al.*, 1994).

2.1.5. . Wildlife resources

The fauna of the Batéké Plateau is highly diverse, comprising mammals, reptiles, birds and fish. It contributes to the food security of the local population, but is under considerable pressure from poverty and, above all, the demographic explosion, which is increasing demand for bushmeat.

2.1.6. . Land use and agricultural activities

On the Batékés plateau, the soils have very limited agricultural value, due to their low water retention capacity and very low level of chemical fertility (Koy, 2007).

Their agricultural use varies widely, but without outside intervention, yields fall as soon as the second crop is planted after the first, after which a fallow period of at least ten years is needed to support a crop again. In general, the soils of the Batéké Plateau are used for annual crops (maize, cassava, groundnuts and cowpeas).

The sandy soils of the closed depressions have virtually no agricultural value; they are sporadically used to grow groundnuts.

With a view to increasing the agricultural potential of the soils of the Plateau des Batékés, the Congolese government, with the help of the European Union and the Hanns-Seidel Foundation, the CADIM (Centre d'Appui au Développement Intégral de Mbankana,), Ibi-Village and more recently the NSTIO project, is promoting the agroforestry system in the savannah environment in the north-east of the Plateau.

These projects are located in the Mampu-Mbankana, IBI and NSTIO sectors, where Acacia legumes (*A. auriculiformis, A. mangium,* etc.) have been introduced to form

17

planted forests that act both as carbon sinks and soil fertilisers, not forgetting the fight against poverty among urban and rural populations.

2.2. . Methods

2.2.1. . Bibliographical approach

The literature search consisted of consulting the various documents available (studies, reports, books, etc.) relating to agroforestry and gender. This section helped to flesh out the problem and prepare the literature review.

2.2.2. . Data collection in the field

Field data collection took place from 23 October to 23 November 2017. Two approaches were used to achieve this. The first involved household surveys using a questionnaire and the second involved focus group discussions using an interview guide.

2.2.3. . Conduct of the household survey

The household was considered as a group of people living in a housing unit under the responsibility of a single person recognised by the other members of the unit as being the head of the household and presenting him/herself as such. This head could be either male or female (ISCO, 2012).

The head of the household may live alone or with his wife or wives or her husband (if female) and their children, as well as collaterals and other persons usually living under the same roof.

The households to be surveyed were selected at random. During sampling, each household had the same probability of being selected. Under these conditions, the drawing of one household was independent of the drawing of any other household in our site.

The survey covered 30 households represented by their heads. The person interviewed in each household depended on availability. The questionnaire was designed to meet the objectives of the study, with both open and closed questions. The survey was conducted using the funnel method.

2.2.4. . Processing and analysis of survey data

The data thus obtained, after manual processing, were analysed using SPSS and Excel 2010 software.

CHAPTER 3

RESULTS AND DISCUSSION

111.1. Socio-demographic characteristics

The data collected during our study are set out in the tables and graphs below.

111.1.1. Type of respondent

Table 1: Gender of respondent

Type of respondent				
Male		Female		Total
Workforce	%	Workforce	%	%
4	13,3	26	86,7	100

The table above shows that 86.7% of respondents were women and 13.3% were men. The low participation of men in the survey can be explained by the impression given by many men that they are very busy.

III.1.2. Age range of respondents

Table 2: Age of respondents

Age of respondent	Workforce	%
18-30 years old	3	10
31- 40 years old	13	43,3
41- 50 years old	13	43,3
51 - 60 years old	1	3,4
61 - 70 years	0	0
Over 70	0	0
Total	30	100

The age groups most represented in our survey are those between 31-40 and 41-50. This can be explained by the fact that these people represent the category that has a lot of burdens (parents with schooling, health care, housing needs, etc.). This is why these age groups, made up of people with the physical strength to carry out agroforestry work, are the best represented in our study.

None of the respondents was over 60. This can be explained by the fact that agroforestry work requires a great deal of physical effort, something that people over 60 are very short of.

1.1.3. 3. Level of education of respondents

The level of education of respondents is shown in the table below.

Table 3: Level of education of respondents

Level of study	Workforce	%
Did not study	6	20,0
Primary	7	23,3
Secondary	16	53,3
Higher/university	1	3,4
Total	30	100

With regard to the respondents' level of education, the results of our survey showed that 53.3% of respondents had secondary education, 23.3% had primary education, 20% had no education and 3.4% had university education. Analysis of these results clearly shows the major obstacle to women's emancipation in a society where education is at a premium.

111.2. Agroforestry activities

111.2.1. Area farmed

The area farmed by each agroforestry operator is shown in the table below.

Table 4: Area farmed by each agroforestry operator

Surface area (ha)	Workforce	%
1	0	0
1 à2,5	0	0
2,6 à 5	2	6,7

21

| More than 5 | 28 | 93,3 |
| Total | 30 | 100 |

The table above shows that 93.3% of respondents farmed an area of more than 5 ha and 6.7% farmed between 2.6 and 5 ha. The results of our study showed that no agroforestry farmer had an area of less than 2.6 ha. The area granted under the NSTIO project depended mainly on the size of the household and also on the farmer's willingness to take care of the area entrusted to him.

111.2.2. Experience in agroforestry

During the survey, all the respondents stated that their experience varied from 1 to 5 years. This can be justified by the fact that they had all been taken on by the project, i.e. the length of their experience depended on when the project started.

111.2.3. Different species grown on our study site

The plant species grown on our study site are: *Acacia auriculiformis*, *Acacia mangium*, *Maesopsis emini*, *Pinus sp*, *Eucalyptus radie*, *Elaeis guinensis* and Citrus. The seedlings came from the project's central nursery (photos below) (except for citrus) and were distributed to farmers. In the field, these seedlings were combined with food and vegetable crops.

Photo 1: Pinus sp. nursery

Photo 2: Acacia mangium nursery

Photo 3: *Eucalyptus radie nursery*
Photo 4: *Maesopsis emini nursery*

Photo 5 : *Nursery Elaeis guineensis* Jacq.

111.2.4. Different food crops associated with trees and oil palm

The food crops associated with the main species are manioc, maize, squash, cowpeas, groundnuts, sesame, peppers and yams. Associated vegetable crops are aubergines, sorrel, nightshade, okra, Voandzou and amaranth.

111.2.5. Reasons for using the agroforestry system

The survey of agroforestry farmers collected information on the reasons that led farmers to adopt the agroforestry system. The majority of farmers practise the agroforestry system to ensure food security, diversify their diet and income, improve soil fertility and, lastly, improve household living conditions.

111.3. Allocation of responsibilities for carrying out agroforestry activities and decision-making

With regard to the financing of the farm, the results showed that 36.7 of the respondents said that it was the man who took the decision, 26.6% said that it was the woman who took the decision and 36.7 confirmed that the decision on financing was taken by mutual agreement between the man and the woman.

With regard to the choice of land and crops to be grown, 36.7% of respondents said that it was the man who made the decision, 30% thought that it was the woman who made the decision and 33.3% confirmed that it was both the man and the woman who made the decision.

With regard to land preparation, 33.3% of respondents said that it was the man who carried out this activity, 26.7 thought that it was the woman who did the land preparation work and 33.3% said that this activity was carried out by both the man and the woman and 6.7% by the children and other family members.

With regard to planting, 6.7% of respondents said that it was the man who carried out this activity, 23.3% thought that it was the woman, and 60% confirmed that it was both the man and the woman. Children and other family members also contribute to this activity.

With regard to farm maintenance, 23.3% of respondents said that it was the woman who did the maintenance, 63.3% confirmed that this activity was carried out by both the man and the woman, and 13.4% thought that maintenance was carried out by the children and other family members.

The results of our study showed that 3.4% of harvesting work is carried out by men, 23.3% by women, 63.3% by both men and women and 10% by children and other family members.

3.3% of processing operations are carried out by men, 40% by women, 50% by both men and women, and 6.7% by children.

The products are sold by men (23.3%), women (43.3%), men and women (33.4%).

The decision on the allocation of income is shared 10% by the man, 10% by the woman and 80% by mutual agreement between the man and the woman.

The results of our survey show that the income generated by the sale of products is kept by the man (16.7%), by the woman (80%) and by both the man and the woman (3.3%).

In the case of the NSTIO project in the Batéké Plateau, of the 20 people involved in the project, there are only two women (one an agricultural engineer and the other an economist).

111.3.1. The Operations Manager

The results of the survey with regard to management responsibility for the operation are presented in the table below.

Table 5: Operations manager

Farm manager	Workforce	%
Men	23	76,6
Woman	7	23,3
Child	0	0
Men and women	0	0
Total	30	100

The table above shows that the head of the farm is the man, with 76.6% of positive responses, and 23.3% of respondents said that the woman was the head of the farm. Despite her many responsibilities in carrying out farm work, the woman is not the head of the farm.

The man is the head, despite his low level of involvement in the farm; social rules and culture have a lot to do with this situation.

111.3.2. Ownership of farmland

The land being farmed was entrusted to the project by the traditional chief, and the project in turn distributed the land to the households. These households automatically became the owners of the land being farmed, as they had been proposed by the customary chief.

111.3.3. Participation in seminars/workshops on agroforestry

With regard to participation in seminars/workshops on agroforestry, 20% of surveys confirmed that it was the man who participated, 16.7% confirmed that it was the woman who participated in the training, and 63.3% confirmed that both the woman and the man participated in the training.

111.3.4. Various topics covered during the course

Topics covered include tree planting, crop association, the benefits of agroforestry, work organisation on an agroforestry farm, results-based management, farm maintenance, pest and disease management, beekeeping, etc.

111.4. Difficulties encountered in agroforestry and solutions envisaged by respondents

The difficulties encountered by agroforestry farmers are: evacuation of products, bush fires, etc. The solutions proposed are road maintenance, firebreaks, etc. The solutions proposed are road maintenance, firebreaks, etc.

Discussion

Gender differs from other development concepts in that it addresses the root causes of social inequalities, i.e. social relationships.

Indeed, life in society requires the establishment of reference standards with which the different social categories (men, women, young, old) identify in order to work together (UN-WOMEN, 2014).

The results of our survey show that agroforestry can play an important role in women's emancipation, and that women's participation in training sessions is an important step towards improving their understanding of the role women play in the production system.

So any action that has an impact on the household will have an impact on production. It is true that African tradition is not based on the emancipation of women, but their contribution to the production system, especially in agriculture, cannot be thrown away.

The various laws relating to agriculture must integrate the gender dimension in terms of access to land, farm management, etc. The results of our study show that men are only effectively involved in preparing the land. The results of our study show that men are only effectively involved in preparing the land, so logically they cannot be the head of the farm or make decisions about the income generated by the farm.

As proposed by Kloeppinger *et al* (2010), the levers that enable women's emancipation and consequently improve their situation must be supported. Women's education and training are of paramount importance. No emancipation and no sustainable agroforestry system can be achieved in conditions where women's education is at a low level.

CHAPTER 4
CONCLUSION AND SUGGESTIONS

The main objective of this study is to promote the involvement of women in agroforestry. Specifically, the study aims to analyse the contribution of agroforestry to women's emancipation.

The results obtained showed that the plant species cultivated on our study site are : *Acacia auriculiformis, Acacia mangium, Maesopsisemini, Pinus sp Eucalyptus radie, Elaeis guineensis* and fruit trees. The seedlings came from the project's central nursery (except for the fruit trees) and were distributed to the farmers.

With regard to the financing of the farm, 36.7% of respondents said that it was the man who took the decision, 26.6% confirmed that it was the woman who took the decision and 36.7% said that the decision on financing was taken by mutual agreement between the man and the woman.

3.3% of processing operations are carried out by men, 40% by women, 50% by both men and women, and 6.7% by children. The products are sold by men (23.3%), women (43.3%), men and women (33.4%). The decision on how to allocate income is made by men (10%), women (10%) and men and women (80%).

The income generated by the sale of products is kept by the woman, but she only plays the role of cashier. Although she is the cashier, in practice the decision to allocate the income rests with the man.

Women are involved in all operations, from site preparation to sales. The volume of work is very high, which can limit her productive capacity. Based on the results of our study, agroforestry can play an important role in women's emancipation. Women's participation in training sessions is an important step towards improving their understanding of the role women play in the production system.

We suggest that further studies be carried out to find the strategies needed to strengthen the position of women in the management of agroforestry operations.

BIBLIOGRAPHICAL REFERENCES

Anonymous, 2010. Guide de l"agroforesterie dans les réglementations agricoles. État des lieux. Chamber of Agriculture.

Berti F., Lebailly P., 2012. African family farming at the heart of the Millennium Development Goals (MDGs). Communication Unité d'Économie et Développement rural Gembloux Agro-Bio Tech - Université de Liège.

Bisiaux F., Peltier R., Muliele J., 2014. Plantation Industrielles et Agroforesterie au service des populations des plateaux Batéké, Mampu en République Démocratique du Congo, RDC, 60 p.

Bultot F., 1950. Atlas climatique du bassin congolais. Publications de l'Institut National pour L'Étude: Agronomique Du Congo. Hors-Série. INÉAC. Brussels.

Bultot F., 1950. Carte des régions climatiques du Congo Belge établie d'après les critères de Koppen. Brussels, Climate Bureau, Communication No. 2. INEAC.

CADIM, 2010. UNDP Ecuador Initiative. Rapport Annuel du Centre d'Appui au Développement Intégral. Mbankana, Combeaud L., Benoit O., 2013. Apiculture et reforestation en RDC, RDC, 155 p.

Dupiez and De Leener, 1997. Gardens and orchards of Africa. Terre et vie, France. ISBN: 2-87105-004-X. 2nd edition. 354p.

FAO, 1989. Sustainable Agricultural Production: Implication for International Agricultural Research. Technical Advisory Committee, CGIAR. FAO Research and Technical Paper No. 4. Rome, Italy: FAO.

FAO, 2017. Forests and Climate Change Programme: the instruments of the United Nations Framework Convention on Climate Change and their potential for Africa's sustainable development, Working Paper FOPW/02/1, http://www.fao.org/docrep/004/Y4000F/y4000f00.htm.

FAO, 2011. Food security and agricultural development in sub-Saharan Africa. Policy Assistance Series 2, Main Report, Rome 2006.

Folly M., 2013. Actions de reforestation/ lutte contre la déforestation. Synergie Apiculture Congo (SYNAPIC), DRC, 50 p.

ISCO, 2012. Analyse de l'Enquête ménage réalisée en 2011 dans 14 territoires de la

Province du Bandundu. Report of the Bandundu Agricultural Development Project PAB DCI 172- 355.

Kloeppinger R., Todd and Manohar Sharma, 2010. Innovations in rural and agricultural financial services, International Food Policy Research Institute and the World Bank, Focus 18. www.ifpri.orgouwww.worldbank.org/ard.

Koy K., 2007. Amélioration de la qualité des sols sableux du plateau des Batéké (RD Congo) par application des matériels géologiques et des déchets organiques industriels locaux. PhD thesis in Earth Sciences, University of GENT, 400 p.

Lallau B., 2004. Poverty, sustainability and choice capacities: Can Central African farmers avoid the vicious circle? Développement durable et territoires, accessed 24 November 2015. URL :
http://developpementdurable.revues.org/1185;DOI:
10.4000/sustainabledevelopment.1185.

Makoko M., Ndembo L. and Nsimba M., 1994. Les caractéristiques pédologiques, mécaniques et stock d'eau du sol, *Revue Zaïroise des Sciences Nucléaires de Kinshasa*, 72-79 pp.

UN-WOMEN, 2014. National development priorities 2017-2021.

Tchunza M., 2010. Apiculture : Une source de revenus, une alternative à la gestion des forêts du Bas- Congo, SNV, RDC, 54 p.

Tshibilondi N., 2005. Enjeux de l'éducation de la femme. Cas des femmes congolaises du Kasaï, Le Harmattan, Paris.

Tshibilondi N., 2009. Genre et situation sociojuridique des femmes en Afrique. Cas des femmes congolaises, Le Harmattan, Paris.

Appendix

Survey questionnaire

CONFIDENTIALITY: All the information you provide will be kept strictly confidential and used for academic purposes only.

I. Identification of the respondent

MODULE 1: IDENTIFYING THE

Questionnaire number: _____ //

Date of interview: / __ / ___ ___ //

Site :...

MODULE 2: SOCIO-DEMOGRAPHIC CHARACTERISTICS

1.1. Age: 18 to 30☐ 31 to 40☐ 41 to 50☐ 51 to 60☐ 61 to 70☐ Over 70 ☐

1.2. Gender: 1. male 2. Female

1.3. Level of education: 1. Not studied☐ 2. Primary ☐

              3. Secondary☐ 4. Higher/University ☐

MODULE 3: AGROFORESTRY ACTIVITIES

3.1. Do you have an agroforestry farm?

1. Yes ☐

2. No ☐

If yes,

3.2. What area is cultivated?

1. Less than 1 ha ☐

2. 1 to 2.5 ha ☐

3. 2.6 to 5 ha ☐

4. More than 5 years ☐

3.3. What is the source of funding for this operation?

1. Household financing ☐

2. Other organisations ☐

3. 3.1. At household level, is the farm manager ?

1. Dad ☐

2. Mum ☐

3. Child(ren) ☐

4. The whole family ☐

4. Other distant member ☐

3.3.2. What is the nature of the support organisations?

1. Project ☐
2. NGO ☐
3. Status ☐
4. Third party ☐

3.3.3. Type of support

1. Granting seeds ☐
2. Granting seedlings ☐
3. Material grants ☐
4. Work subsidy ☐
5. Other, please specify ☐
6. Support institutions ☐

1.4. Who owns the land being farmed

1. Dad ☐
2. Mum ☐
3. Mum and Dad ☐
4. Children ☐
4. Family legacy ☐
5. Other family members ☐
6. Support institutions **(project)** ☐

3.4.1. If this is the project, what type of contract do you have with the supporting institution(s)?

1. Don ☐
2. Metayage ☐
3. Farming ☐
4. Other, please specify ☐

3.5. Time: how long have you been in business?

1. Less than a year ☐
2. 1 to 5 years ☐
3. 5 to 10 years ☐
4. 10 years or more ☐

3.6. What different tree species do you associate with food crops?

Quote

the ....

3.7. What different food crops do you associate with trees?

Quote it ....

3.8. Why do you associate these trees with crops? ....

MODULE 4: SHARING RESPONSIBILITY FOR ACTIVITIES
AGROFORESTRY AND DECISION-MAKING

Activities	Decision-maker/Activity manager					
	Dad	Mum	Mum and Dad	Children	Family member(s)	Other
1. Financing operations						
2. Choice of land and crops						
3. Site preparation						
4. Planting						
5. Maintenance						
6. Harvest						
7. Product processing						
8. Sale of products						
9. Allocation of income						
10. Revenue management						

MODULE 5: EQUIPMENT USED

5.2. What production equipment and machinery do you use to carry out your activities?

N°	Activities/work	Equipment/machinery
1		
2		
3		
4		
5		
6		
7		
8		
9		
10		

MODULE 6: TAKING PART IN TRAINING COURSES/SEMINARS/WORKSHOPS ON AGROFORESTRY

6.1. Have you taken part in training/seminars/workshops on agroforestry?

1. Yes ☐

2. No ☐

6.2. Who took part?

1. Dad ☐

2. Mum ☐

3. Children ☐

4. The whole family ☐

5. Other distant member ☐

6.3. What topics are covered?

Name them:

1 :..

2 :..

3 : ....

4 : ....

MODULE 7: DIFFICULTIES ENCOUNTERED AND SOLUTIONS ENVISAGED

7.1. What are the various difficulties you encounter on your farm?

1 : ....

2 : ....

3 : ....

4 : ....

5 : ....

7.2. What are the recommended solutions?

1 : ....

2 : ....

3 : ....

4 : ....

5 : ....

7.3. As women, are the activities of this project gender-balanced?

1. Yes ☐

2. No ☐

If so, how? ....

If not, why not?...

7.4. Your last words :...

Thank you for your availability

Milton Keynes UK
Ingram Content Group UK Ltd.
UKHW011147010424
440421UK00001B/340

9 786207 301423